Fluff and Nip

Note on the Revised Edition

HAPPY VENTURE was conceived and has been validated as a basic teaching method, and as such has proved outstandingly successful. Our language is a living one, however, and so certain expressions appearing in the original edition have now gone out of use.

Before his death in 1969, Professor Schonell was actively engaged in discussion with the publishers about the revision of the entire series. Unfortunately he was not able to undertake this before he died.

After consultations with practising teachers throughout the country and abroad, it became apparent to the publishers that the principles on which the series was based had not altered, but that minor changes to up-date the text could be made without affecting the well-tested structure of the series.

Accordingly, in this book, teachers will find:
'a' and 'g' altered to script 'ɑ' and 'g'; new illustrations throughout; 'Mother' altered to 'Mummy'.

The publishers acknowledge the help and advice of Miss Angela Ridsdale of Toorak Teachers' College, Malvern, Victoria, Australia, in the preparation of the Australian edition of this series.

OLIVER & BOYD
Robert Stevenson House
1-3 Baxter's Place
Leith Walk
Edinburgh EH1 3BB
A Division of Longman Group Ltd.

First published   1939
Second Edition   1958
Revised Edition   1971
Twelfth impression 1984

ISBN 0 05 002378 0

Printed in Hong Kong by
Sheck Wah Tong Printing Press Ltd

Happy Venture
Introductory Book

Fluff and Nip

FRED J. SCHONELL
and IRENE SERJEANT

Illustrated by Will Nickless

OLIVER AND BOYD: EDINBURGH

Here is Dick.

Here is Nip.

Here is Dora.

Here is Fluff.

Here is Nip.
Nip is a dog.

I see Nip.
I see a dog.

Here is Dick.
Run, Dick, run.

Nip is a dog.
Nip, run to Dick.

See Dora run.

Here is Jane.
I see Jane.
Dora has Jane.

Here is Nip.
Dick has the dog.
I see Nip and Jane.

This is Jane.
Jane is in the mud.
Jane fell in the mud.

This is the dog.
Nip, run to Dora.
The dog has Jane.

Can you see Nip?
Can you see the mud?
The mud is wet.

Nip, the dog, is wet.
Nip, run to Dora.
Dora has Jane.

I am the cat.
I am Dora's cat.
A cat can run.

Can you see the dog?

This is the dog.
This is Nip.

Nip and Fluff run to Dick.

This is Fluff.
Fluff is a cat.

Fluff is in the tree.
Dora is with the cat.

I am Nip, the dog.
I run to the tree.

I see Dora and the cat.
Dora fell with the cat.

The dog runs to Mummy.

Mummy runs with Dick
to see Dora.

Mummy, I am wet.
I am in this mud.
Fluff is in the mud.

You can see Mummy
   with Dick and Dora.
Dick sits by Mummy.
Dora sits with Dick.

The cat sits by the tree.
The mud by this tree
   is wet.

Fluff, the cat,
  is in the tree.

Nip, the dog,
  runs to Jane.

Mummy is with Dick
and Nip.

Dick has a ball.
The ball is big.
Dick runs with the ball.

Nip, see the ball.
Nip, the dog, runs
    with Dick to the ball.

Nip sits by the ball.

It is fun to see
the dog with the ball.

Can you play, Nip?
I can play with you.
I can play with the ball.

Nip runs to the ball
and sits with it.

Here is Jack.
Jack can play with Dick.

Dora can bring Jane.
It is fun to play
    with Dora and Jane.

Nip, bring the big ball
    and play with it.

I see a big tree.
The ball is in
 the tree.
Jack will bring
 the ball.

Here is the ball.
It is a big big ball.
You can play
 with this big ball.

It is fun in the
   tree.
Jack is with Dick.

The big ball fell
   in the wet mud.

Mummy has the
   ball.
Dick and Jack
   will get the ball.

Jack is in the tree.
Dick is in the tree.

Dora will not get in
    the big tree.
She runs to get Jane.

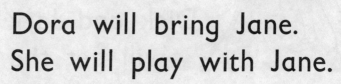

Dora will bring Jane.
She will play with Jane.

Nip sits by the ball.
Fluff will play with Nip.
She will get the big ball.

Big dog, I can see you.
I will take the ball
and I will play with it.

It is fun to play.

This is the ball.
Jack has the big ball.
Jack and Dick will play.

The ball fell in the mud.
Nip, get the ball.
Bring the ball to Jack.

It is fun to see Nip
run with the ball.

Here is Mummy.

Mummy sits by the tree.
She will not take the ball.

Dora will bring Fluff.
Nip and Fluff will run.
Run, run, run.
It is fun to run.

Word List

This list contains all the new words used in the INTRODUCTORY BOOK. There are 44 words in all and the numbers refer to the pages on which the words are first used. There is an average of less than 2 new words per page, that is, 1 new word to every 14 words of reading matter, so that adequate repetition has been allowed for. Material for revision is provided on pages 22, 30 and 31.

The words in this book form a definite preparation for BOOK ONE.

5 here
is
Dick
Nip

6 Dora
Fluff

7 a
dog

8 I
see

9 run
to

10 Jane
has

11 the
and

12 this
in
mud
fell

14 can
you
wet

16 am
cat
Dora's

18 tree
with

19 runs
Mummy

21 sits
by

23 ball
big

24 it
fun
play

25 Jack
bring

26 will

27 get

28 not
she

29 take

HAPPY VENTURE

A carefully-graded course with rigorous control of vocabulary, **Happy Venture** is a firm favourite with many teachers.

Happy Venture Teacher's Manual offers many practical suggestions.   0 05 002473 6

Reading Fun forms a bridge between oral and printed words.   0 05 002525 2

Happy Venture Readers combine the merits of phonic, whole word and sentence methods of teaching.

Approach Book	0 05 002377 2
Introductory Book	0 05 002378 0
Book 1 (Play Time)	0 05 002379 9
Book 2 (Our Friends)	0 05 002380 2
Book 3 (Growing Up)	0 05 002381 0
Book 4 (Holiday Time)	0 05 002382 9

Happy Venture Playbooks are colour-linked to the basic readers and offer more reading practice at each level.

Introductory (Hide and Seek)	0 05 002383 7
Playbook 1 (Story Time)	0 05 003384 5
Playbook 2 (Saturday Play)	0 05 002385 3
Playbook 3 (Now for some Stories)	0 05 002386 1
Playbook 4 (Far and Wide)	0 05 002387 X

Happy Venture Workbooks are to be used with the corresponding reader.

Approach	0 05 002388 8	Workbook 2	0 05 002391 8
Introductory	0 05 002389 6	Workbook 3	0 05 002392 6
Workbook 1	0 05 002390 X	Workbook 4	0 05 002393 4

Happy Venture Library Books contain lively and imaginative stories making use of the vocabulary introduced in the basic readers.

For Introductory Reader	Books 1-5	0 05 000360 7
For Reader 1	Books 6-10	0 05 002532 5
For Reader 2	Books 11-15	0 05 002533 3
For Reader 3	Books 16-21	0 05 000363 1
For Reader 4	Books 22-27	0 05 000364 X

ISBN 0 05 002378 0

Are We Nearly There Yet?

Wrestling with Issues in the Life of Faith

Gareth Evans